LFA Health Ar

CW00828550

T'ai Chi Stick
Movements 1 – 150

Explained in an easy to follow format

By Sheila Dickinson
President of the LFA Health Arts

Benefits:-
Helps to improve balance and co-ordination
Helps to improve joint mobility
Eases Stress
Provides Relaxation

Printed and published in Great Britain by

STAIRWAY
DISTRIBUTION
LTD.

P O BOX 19,
HEDON,
HULL
HU12 8YR

First Published 2001

Published by Stairway Distribution Limited
PO Box 19, Hedon. Hull. HU12 8YR
www.leefamilyarts.com

Please consult your Doctor before taking part in the
following exercise programme.
The LFA and Stairway Distribution Ltd disclaim any
liability for loss or injury in connection with the advice
and exercises included in this book.

Acknowledgements

To the past Masters of our Arts - we offer our sincere thanks!

Books by the same author:-

T'AI CHI FORM	(MOVEMENTS 1 TO 140)
T'AI CHI DANCE	(MOVEMENTS 1 TO 184)
T'AI CHI STICK	(MOVEMENTS 1 TO 150)
T'AI CHI SILK	(MOVEMENTS 1 TO 156)
T'AI CHI SWORD	(MOVEMENTS 1 TO 108)
T'AI CHI NUNCHAKU	(MOVEMENTS 1 TO 150)
T'AI CHI FAN	(MOVEMENTS 1 TO 150)

VIDEOS by the same author:-

T'AI CHI FORM	(MOVEMENTS 1 TO 50)
T'AI CHI DANCE	(MOVEMENTS 1 TO 50)
T'AI CHI STICK	(MOVEMENTS 1 TO 50)
T'AI CHI SILK	(MOVEMENTS 1 TO 50)
T'AI CHI SWORD	(MOVEMENTS 1 TO 50)

Available from: -

Stairway Distribution Limited
P O Box 19
Hedon
Hull
HU12 8YR
Tel / Fax 01482 896063

Or visit our Website www.leefamilyarts.com

CONTENTS

Foreword

My position as President of the Lee Family Arts started in January 1995. Since that time, I have had the privilege to guide my fellow instructors in all aspects of LFA T'ai Chi, and I have worked hard to reach as many people as possible, so that everyone may gain from the many health benefits of our Arts.

I would not be writing this book today without the guidance and patience of my late Grand Master Chee Soo, who spent most of his life teaching the Lee Family Arts. Chee Soo is in my thoughts constantly and I offer my sincere thanks for receiving the benefit of his wisdom and understanding.

Chee Soo wrote five books published by the Aquarian Press, sadly at the time of writing, only one title remains in print today 'The Chinese Art of T'ai Chi Ch'uan'. In this book he traces the history of the Lee Style back to Ho-Hsieh Lee circa 1,000BC. It is stated that the Lee Family have always been Taoists and that the Lee Style is a Yin and Yang style, this means that everything within it is in complete balance and harmony.

Chee Soo occasionally spoke of his own Grand Master, Chan Kam Lee and told of how they had met during 1934 in Hyde Park in London. In those days there were very few Oriental people in London and the two became friends. It was a friendship that would change Chee Soo's life forever. After Chan Kam Lee's death, Chee Soo dedicated himself to maintaining the knowledge and wisdom he had learnt from Chan Kam Lee.

While staying with my family and my self, Chee Soo talked to me about the future of the Lee Family Arts and the direction he wished them to take. On Monday the 16th May 1994 Chee Soo asked me to give him my word that I would not let the Lee Family Arts die.

Sadly Chee Soo died on the 29th August 1994.

It is with the greatest respect to Chee Soo that I offer my own writings and understanding of the lessons he taught me.

The names of Instructors who have trained, qualified and still maintain their own training can be obtained from the Lee Family Arts official register of qualified instructors. The LFA can only vouch for the quality and content of what is taught within an official LFA registered class.

The Lee Family Arts have been tried and tested for thousands of years before we were born. The people who teach them are merely caretakers, who have the privilege of maintaining the Arts, and witnessing them helping others.

This book teaches you the first one hundred and fifty movements of the LFA T'ai Chi Stick. There are two hundred and seventy movements in total and these will be explained in further publications.

The Lee Family Arts will always be known as a Family Art and it is a family that grows in numbers daily. In concluding, I would like to say a very special welcome to you!

How Important Is Your Health?

Although Western medicine has made great leaps forward over the past century, people are still plagued by aches and pains. There are those who accept it as part of getting old and there are people like yourselves who are taking the time to read this book and practise the LFA Health Arts.

In our Arts we teach much more than basic exercise, we teach you how to enhance your body's natural energy called Chi energy. This is the body's internal energy, Chi energy is known as yin energy or micro – cosmic energy. It is within everyone from the moment we are born until the day we die.

The LFA know of many ways to develop this energy, one of which is by practising our K'ai Men exercises. They are taught within all of our classes. K'ai Men means open door and our exercises literally open up the channels between the mind, body and spirit, so that all can work together in harmony.

Through regular practise of LFA K'ai Men and our Specialised Breathing Exercises, you will begin to notice everything around you and appreciate the miracles that are taking place even as you read this book.

Every one should be forewarned of the misuse of the senses, for it takes away vital energy from your body. Never try to harm any one in thought word or deed, an easy sentence to write and read, far more difficult to put into practise.

Purification of the mind is achieved by thinking only good thoughts. It is sometimes hard to accept things on face value, especially when it does not make sense to you. Anger, hurt, hatred and jealousy are all products of a troubled mind. In other words it is like a sickness, for example, an aching back or any other ache or pain. Eating and drinking the Chang Ming way should be part of your life if you are truly interested in good health. Changing your eating habits will help to improve your circulation and ease a troubled mind. It also helps to improve the quality of your bones, tissues and organs. Whatever your diet, it is important to eat slowly, chewing your food really well will help to improve your digestion. People who eat the Chang Ming way do not feel so tired and find they have more energy to enjoy other areas of their lives.

Through regular training in all aspects of our Arts, your Chi and Li energies may be developed to such an extent that you can help others. This is a very advanced stage and should not be attempted by the novice, for they may take more energy from the suffering, than they are able to give in return.

Chi and Li energies can be used for healing in a similar way to acupuncture. The fingers and palms are used on the meridians instead of using needles.

Chi energy is your own personal energy, it is required for the support system of your body and only you can develop it and improve it. Your Chi energy moves along the lines of your meridians. A person with highly developed Chi energy, experiences very few illnesses. Li energy (macro – cosmic energy which permeates through everything in the cosmos), moves through the tissues and the bones. It is the energy that is vital to the life of your spirit. We teach exercises to enable you to harness this energy to improve the quality of your life.

Within the LFA we also teach healing by meditation, this is another advanced stage of our Arts and takes many years to master. Meditation takes many forms and will be taught only to the students who have grasped the basic understanding of developing and harnessing their energies.

Practising the Lee Family Arts is a life times work, yet it is a work of great interest and pleasure. Which can be enjoyed in harmony with modern day living. Many will place their foot on the path, and we hope they will have the commitment to complete the journey.

Within the LFA we also teach:-

T'ai Chi Form, Dance, Stick, Silk, Sword, Nunchaku, Fan, Broad Sword, Umbrella, Knife, Chop Sticks, Taoist Walk, K'ai Men - Chi Kung, Breathing Exercises, Awareness Techniques, Feng Shou (self defence) Chi Shu and Chang Ming (diet).

Breath Of Life

How long can we exist without food or water? The answer is many days. How long can we live without breathing? Try it, I guarantee it will not be long before you are gasping for air.

If breathing is so important to us, doesn't it make sense to look after our lungs and body so that we can enjoy a full and happy life.

I am not about to embark on a Campaign of stop smoking, the facts are out there and it is a matter of personal choice.

Instead let me ask you, do you breathe correctly? Do you use all of your lungs? Or do you use only a small part of them? Do you know how to breathe correctly? In our classes we teach you how to use your lungs correctly, learning when a yang breath is required (breathing deep into the lower part of your lungs), and when a yin breath is required (breathing into the upper part of your lungs).

The latter breath is the most commonly used in the West. Regrettably it allows toxins to build up in the lower part of your lungs, storing up problems for a later date.

Correct breathing uses the whole of the lungs, although in certain exceptions a yin breath is required. For example in the LFA T'ai Chi Dance where it is combined with flowing movements to activate and stimulate the mind, while at the same time gathering and harnessing Li energy.

Yang breathing on the other hand, is used in our LFA T'ai Chi Form where it helps to calm the mind and heal the body, by soothing stress and expelling toxins. This in turn encourages the free flow of Chi energy.

In our T'ai Chi Stick Set we use both yin and yang breathing.

Asthma is becoming more and more wide spread. Modern day research blames pollution, among other things. In our classes, students who suffer from asthma find that after practising LFA T'ai Chi for two or more weeks, they no longer need to use their inhalers (although we still suggest you carry them with you). We are not in competition with Western medicine, we simply show you ways to help yourself. After all you have the freedom of choice, it is up to you how you choose to look after your health.

It is important to be able to breathe deeply to cleanse the toxins from the blood in the body. If the blood is not cleansed then waste products accumulate in the blood stream causing deterioration and a weakening of the whole body. In turn, your resistance to infection will become low and you may find yourself suffering from many ailments.

In our K'ai Men Book you will find easy to follow exercises to help improve the quality of your health and the understanding of your body.

A simple breathing exercise, is to sit quietly in a chair. Place both hands on your abdomen and gently expand your stomach as you breathe in through your nose and gently contract your stomach as you breathe out through your mouth.

If you suffer from chest related aliments such as emphysema or bronchitis, then please pay attention to your breathing before it is too late.

Throughout the whole of the LFA, we are devoted to helping people, we encourage you to start slowly. This is not a race, the speed with which you progress should be the right speed for you. EVERYONE IS AN INDIVIDUAL and there is no strain in LFA T'ai Chi. Take the first step and start to practise deep breathing today. With practise students of LFA T'ai Chi may find a brighter tomorrow.

Taoist Walk

The Taoist Walk is an extremely important part of the LFA health training because it moves the weight from one leg to another in a special and subtle way.

Not only is one leg working while the other one rests, but the working leg is the Yang leg and the resting leg is the Yin leg.

The weight is moved from one leg to the other <u>before</u> you try and alter the position of your foot.

Start with your feet slightly wider than shoulder width apart, toes pointing forwards.

Both hands are held with the palms facing each other.

1/ Drift your weight across to your right side, your right knee bends, your hips and your bottom move across to the right side.

2/ Now take a very small step forwards with your left foot, placing your heel down first. Allow your left knee to bend, move your hips and bottom across to the left. Keep your right leg straight, do not lock your right knee.

Practise walking across the room in this manner. People suffering from back, hip, knee and ankle problems, reap great benefits from practising the Taoist Walk.

We use the Taoist Walk in all of our form sets. With practise it can be incorporated into your every day walk (so that it is undetectable), only you will know the benefits you are receiving each time you place one foot in front of the other.

The Taoist Walk helps to move your Chi energy into the lower part of your body. In the West we tend to carry a lot of congestion around the pelvic area, this stagnation leads to the above mentioned problems. So it is a good idea to learn to walk the Taoist way.

Please try it for yourself, especially if you wake up in the morning feeling stiff, a few minutes practising the Taoist Walk could help to make you feel like a new man or woman.

Etiquette

The etiquette is something that has been handed down through the centuries along with the T'ai Chi, I personally feel it represents a respect for the Arts we are practising and the ancient Masters to whom we owe so much.

When entering or leaving a training hall, a student should bow to the room. This bow consists of bending forwards from the waist, at the same time both palms rest on your thighs.

If you arrive after a class has already started you should walk round to the front of the hall, bow to the person taking the class and wait for them to bow to you in return (using the bow explained below).

At the beginning of a class the bow consists of placing your right arm on top of your left in front of your body, your right hand palm faces down, and your left palm faces up.

When training with a partner you should both bow to each other at the start and finish (using the same bow as when entering and leaving the training room).

If an instructor offers you guidance with your training, you should bow to them after they have finished teaching you, (again using the bow for entering and leaving the training room).

LFA T'ai Chi Stick Set

The LFA Stick set is a sequence of gentle movements designed to improve your health, balance, co-ordination and reflexes. It is important to progress slowly, your progress does not relate to the quantity of movements, it relates to the quality of the movements you practise. It is important that you apply the principles of the Taoist Walk to your movements (see section on the Taoist Walk), this helps to ensure that there is no strain on your body.

We normally practise our Stick Set using a broom handle, however if you are limited by the area of space you have to practise in, try using half a broom handle. When holding your stick keep your grip light so that the stick may move freely between your hands.

If you have difficulty with your balance, do not try to use the stances which require you to stand on one leg, merely rest the ball of your foot on the ground (Cat stance).

Most of all, your practise should be enjoyable, our Stick set uses every part of the body, if you are new to regular exercise, practise only a few movements at a time. Gradually your stamina will improve and you will be able to practise for longer.

The advantage of practising LFA T'ai Chi over other types of exercise is that not only does it exercise the physical body it also works on the internal body, helping to keep all of your organs healthy. At the same time we use special breathing techniques to improve the functioning of your lungs. The memory is also exercised, T'ai Chi is known as the Supreme Ultimate, it gives the mind body and spirit a complete work out without strain.

There is a saying in the West "If you don't use it you lose it", our answer to this is "Practise LFA T'ai Chi to keep every part of you in good working order".

I am frequently asked how often should people practise, there is no one answer, we are all different. However the more you put into LFA T'ai Chi, the more you will get out of it. For example a person who attends one class a week and does not practise until the next class will not receive the same benefit as the person who practises a little every day.

The beauty of LFA T'ai Chi is that it takes only a few minutes to practise the movements you need, yet the rewards are one hundred fold.

LFA T'ai Chi Stances

From the beginning of your training, the LFA emphasise the need for good stances. Stances provide your roots, without correct weight distribution and good balance you will fall over.

The body should not be held rigidly, nor should it be to laid back, strive for the middle path. To achieve this takes many hours of practise.

My late Master described the body as a tree, the legs are the roots and the arms are the branches. Each has its own job to do, while at the same time each is separate, yet each is part of the other. This is another example of how Yin and Yang works.

Although you are probably eager to press on and learn the movements of our stick set. I advise you to take some time to familiarise yourself with the names of our stances and the correct weight distribution for each one.

From the moment you start to practise LFA T'ai Chi, you are beginning to use your Chi energy. In the LFA we teach you how to connect valuable energy points within your own body. The LFA do not promise carrots they cannot deliver. We also have specialised breathing techniques to harness the Li energy, which is 'macro-cosmic' energy or the energy of the Universe. Li energy is also known as Yang energy, it is the external energy. Students attending our day courses become more aware of their own Chi energy, sometimes known as internal energy or Yin energy, it is the energy within your own body. The LFA can teach you how to gain control over both energies to help you improve the quality of your life.

It is a good idea to practise the stances in front of a mirror, if you attend a regular class your instructor will be able to advise you and correct your stances. For those of you who are unable to attend classes, take the time to make sure you are comfortable with each posture before you move on to the next.

Bear Stance

Bear stance is achieved by standing with your feet shoulder width apart. Your body should be relaxed with no tension. Both of your arms hang loosely by your side. Your eyes should be looking straight ahead.

We use Bear stance at the beginning of all our form sets for the Prepare position.

Cat Stance

To achieve a Right Cat stance, the left leg is bent at the knee, the heel is raised on your right foot. The ball of the right foot rests lightly on the floor with eighty percent of your weight on your left leg.

To achieve Left Cat stance, the right leg is bent at the knee, the heel is raised on your left foot. The ball of the left foot rests lightly on the floor with eighty percent of your weight on your right leg.

23

Chicken Stance

To achieve a Right Chicken stance turn ninety degrees to your right. Now place most of your weight onto your right leg (bending the knee), next bend and lower your left knee towards the floor. This is quite a strong stance, it is important that you listen to your own body and do not strain.

To achieve Left Chicken stance turn ninety degrees to your left. Now place most of your weight onto your left leg (bending the knee), next bend and lower your right knee towards the floor. This is quite a strong stance, again it is important that you listen to your own body and **do not** strain.

Crane Stance

To achieve a Right Crane stance move your weight onto your left leg (bending your left knee slightly to aid your balance). At the same time raise your right leg (bending your right knee) until your thigh is parallel

with the floor. Students who have difficulty balancing should use a Cat stance for movements that require one leg to be lifted off the floor.

To achieve a Left Crane stance take your weight onto your right leg (bending your right knee slightly to aid your balance). At the same time raise your left leg (bending your left knee).

Crossed Legs Stance

To achieve Right Crossed Legs stance, bend your left knee slightly. Now cross your right leg in front of and slightly beyond your left leg, raise the heel of your right foot.

To achieve Left Crossed Legs stance, bend your right knee slightly. Now cross your left leg in front of and slightly beyond your right leg, raise the heel of your left foot.

Dog Stance

To achieve Right Dog stance, take your weight onto your left leg (bending the knee slightly to aid your balance). At the same time extend and raise your right leg forwards, your leg should be at a height that is comfortable to you with out strain.

To achieve Left Dog stance, take your weight onto your right leg (bending the knee slightly to aid your balance). At the same time extend and raise your left leg forwards.

Dragon Stance

To achieve a Right Dragon stance step forwards from either a bear or eagle stance. It is important not to over step, make sure you have a good gap width ways between your feet.

Drift your weight over to your right side, so that the weight is spread between your right hip, knee and ankle. Eighty percent of your weight should be on your right leg, your left leg should be straight although not locked.

To achieve a Left Dragon stance follow the same procedure as above this time stepping forwards with your left leg.

28

Duck Stance

To achieve a Right Duck stance from Eagle stance step behind with your left foot, placing your heel down first. Now drift your weight onto your left leg (bending your knee), your right leg should be straight, although not locked.

To achieve a Left Duck stance from Eagle stance step back with your right foot, placing your heel down first. Now drift your weight onto your right leg (bending your knee), your left leg should be straight, although not locked.

Eagle Stance

Eagle stance, place both heels together, toes pointing slightly outwards. Your weight should be evenly balanced between both legs.

Hawk Stance

To achieve a Right Hawk stance, move your weight onto your left leg (bending your knee slightly to aid your balance). Next move your right leg out directly behind you (bending your body forward to create a natural line between your leg and spine). Please remember there should be no strain, listen to your own body. To achieve a Left Hawk stance, move your weight onto your right leg (bending your knee slightly to aid your balance). Next move your left leg out directly behind you.

Horse Stance

To achieve a Right Horse stance take your weight onto your left leg (bending the knee slightly to aid your balance). Now take your right leg out sideways (see photograph). To achieve a Left Horse stance take your weight onto your right leg (bending the knee slightly to aid your balance). Now take your left leg out sideways.

Leopard Stance

To achieve a Right Leopard stance take a pace off sideways to your right (bending your right knee and drifting your weight across). At the same time straighten your left leg.

To achieve a Left Leopard stance take a pace off sideways to your left (bending your left knee and drifting your weight across). At the same time straighten your right leg.

Monkey Stance

To achieve a Right Monkey stance step back with your left leg (bending your left knee). Your right leg is straight with the toes of your right foot raised.

To achieve a Left Monkey stance step back with your right leg (bending your right knee). Your left leg is straight with the toes of your left foot raised.

Riding Horse Stance

Riding Horse stance, both feet are slightly wider than shoulder width apart (both knees bent) your weight should be evenly distributed between both legs.

Scissors Stance

To achieve a Right Scissors stance drift your weight onto your left leg (bending your knee slightly). Now cross your right leg behind and slightly beyond your left leg, next raise the heel of your right foot.

To achieve a Left Scissors stance drift your weight onto your right leg (bending your knee slightly). Now cross your left leg behind and slightly beyond your right leg, next raise the heel of your left foot.

Snake Stance

To achieve a Right Snake stance take a small pace forwards with your right leg. Both knees are slightly bent, your weight is evenly distributed between both legs.

To achieve a Left Snake stance take a small pace forwards with your left leg. Both knees are slightly bent, your weight is evenly distributed between both legs.

Stork Stance

To achieve a Right Stork stance take your weight onto your left leg (bending your left knee slightly to aid your balance). Now raise and bend your right leg taking your foot behind.

To achieve a Left Stork stance take your weight onto your right leg (bending your right knee slightly to aid your balance). Now raise and bend your left leg taking your foot behind.

Stances 1 - 150

1	Eagle
2	Riding Horse
3	Left Dragon
4	Left Cat
5	Left Crane
6	Left Dragon
7	Right Crane
8	Right Dragon
9	Left Scissors
10	Left Dragon
11	Right Scissors
12	Bear
13	Riding Horse
14	Right Crane
15	Left Dragon
16	Left Duck
17	Right Dragon
18	Right Snake
19	Left Crane
20	Left Dragon
21	Right Dragon
22	Left Scissors
23	Right Scissors
24	Right Crane
25	Left Monkey

26	Right Dragon
27	Right Dragon
28	Left Dragon
29	Right Duck
30	Right Duck
31	Left Cat
32	Left Crane
33	Left Dragon
34	Riding Horse
35	Left Crane
36	Left Dragon
37	Right Crane
38	Riding Horse
39	Left Scissors
40	Left Dragon
41	Right Cat
42	Left Crane
43	Left Crane
44	Left Scissors
45	Left Dragon
46	Left Cat
47	Left Crane
48	Left Dragon
49	Left Duck
50	Eagle
51	Left Dragon

52	Right Scissors
53	Left Leopard
54	Left Cat
55	Right Duck
56	Left Duck
57	Right Scissors
58	Left Leopard
59	Right Crossed Legs
60	Right Leopard
61	Right Crane
62	Right Crane
63	Right Dragon
64	Left Duck
65	Left Crane
66	Left Leopard
67	Right Dragon
68	Right Dragon
69	Left Cat
70	Right Dog
71	Left Stork
72	Right Stork
73	Right Dragon
74	Right Leopard
75	Right Crane
76	Right Hawk
77	Riding Horse

78	Right Crane
79	Right Scissors
80	Left Leopard
81	Right Crane
82	Right Hawk
83	Right Dog
84	Left Chicken
85	Right Duck
86	Left Horse
87	Right Dragon
88	Left Stork
89	Left Stork
90	Left Dragon
91	Right Duck
92	Right Duck
93	Left Crane
94	Left Leopard
95	Right Dragon
96	Right Dragon
97	Left Cat
98	Right Dog
99	Riding Horse
100	Riding Horse
101	Right Crane
102	Right Dog
103	Right Scissors

104	Right Dragon
105	Left Stork
106	Right Crane
107	Right Dragon
108	Left Hawk
109	Left Dog
110	Left Dragon
111	Riding Horse
112	Right Horse
113	Left Stork
114	Riding Horse
115	Left Scissors
116	Riding Horse
117	Left Stork
118	Riding Horse
119	Left Scissors
120	Right Horse
121	Right Stork
122	Left Duck
123	Right Duck
124	Left Duck
125	Right Duck
126	Riding Horse
127	Riding Horse
128	Left Hawk
129	Left Hawk

130	Left Dragon
131	Right Dragon
132	Left Dragon
133	Right Dog
134	Right Dragon
135	Right Chicken
136	Left Scissors
137	Riding Horse
138	Bear
139	Left Crane
140	Left Scissors
141	Right Leopard
142	Left Crossed Legs
143	Left Leopard
144	Right Stork
145	Right Dog
146	Left Hawk
147	Eagle
148	Eagle
149	Eagle
150	Eagle

Prepare

Start in Eagle stance, heels together toes pointing slightly outwards. Hold your stick in your right hand, allow your left hand to hang loosely by your side.

Take a pace out sideways to your left, feet shoulder width apart (Bear stance), placing your heel down first.

In LFA T'ai Chi we always place the heel down first.

This is because our Arts are based on Chinese medicine, placing the heel down first ensures the channels open in the correct order.

Your stick is held in your right hand, your left hand hangs loosely by your side.

Number 1

Draw your left foot to your right foot, into Eagle stance. To do this, your weight moves slightly to your right. Once your left leg stops, centre your weight.

The stick remains in the same position as in Prepare.

Number 2

From Eagle stance, take a pace off sideways to your left (heel down first), feet slightly wider than shoulder width apart. Bend both knees, you are now in Riding Horse stance.

At the same time as you start to move your feet, circle the stick round in front of your body with your right hand. Take hold of your stick with your left hand as well as your right. The left hand is below your right hand. Allow your wrist to droop on your right hand (see photograph).

Number 3

From Riding Horse stance, allow your weight to drift across to the right hand side. Then step forwards with your left foot. Your weight should now drift across to the left, at the same time bend your left knee and straighten your right leg. Eighty percent of your weight should be on your left side. The weight should be

evenly distributed between the hip, knee and ankle. It is important that you have a gap between your feet to ensure good balance. You are now in Left Dragon Stance.

At the same time as your feet start to move, change the hand position on your right hand so that the palm faces away from you thumb pointing downwards. Circle the stick in your right hand down towards your right side. The stick finishes angled upwards from your right hip (see photograph) your left hand palm is facing down.

Number 4

From Left Dragon Stance, drift the weight across to your right side at the same time bend your right knee. Draw your left foot in flat to the floor (not too far), then raise the heel of your left foot. You are now in

Left Cat stance.

At the same time as you start to move your feet, circle your stick up and over to the left side of your body (your hands stay in the same position on the stick). Your stick finishes angled upwards from your left hip, left hand low – right hand high (see photograph).

Number 5

From Left Cat stance raise your left leg into the air with your left knee bent and your thigh parallel to the floor you are now in Left Crane Stance. Your right leg is slightly bent to help your balance, if you feel unable

to balance, then keep the ball of your left foot resting lightly on the floor.

At the same time as you start to move your feet, change the hand position on your left hand so that your palm faces upwards. Then circle your right arm downwards and your left arm upwards. Your stick should finish in the vertical position, inside your left thigh. Your left arm should be nearest the top of your stick (see photograph).

Number 6

From Left Crane stance, step forward and place your left heel on the floor, you are now stepping into Left Dragon stance. Remember to drift the weight back to the left side, sharing your weight between your hip, knee and ankle. Straighten your right leg (do not lock

it). Keep a gap width ways between your feet to ensure a good solid stance without strain. It is important not to strain the body by over stepping.

At the same time as you step, your right hand moves forward. Your left hand moves near to your left shoulder before your right hand follows a semicircular path, keep circling over and down, back towards your right hip. The stick finishes angled upwards from your right hip (see photograph).

Number 7

From Left Dragon stance, drift your weight back on to your right side, bending your right knee. Next turn your left foot ninety degrees to the left (pivoting on your left heel). Drift your weight on to your left leg bending your left knee slightly, now raise your right leg into the air with your right knee bent, thigh parallel

to the floor. You are now in Right Crane stance.

At the same time, still holding your stick, circle your right hand up and over onto your left shoulder (palm facing up), your left hand is extended forwards from your left shoulder still holding the stick (see photograph).

Number 8

From Right Crane stance, step forwards into Right Dragon stance. Drifting your weight across to the right side, remember to place your heel down first, bend your right knee and straighten your left leg. If you find a stance is uncomfortable please consult your instructor.

At the same time, keep hold of your stick as you circle your right arm over and underneath your left armpit. Your left arm finishes extended forwards. (see photograph).

Number 9

From Right Dragon stance, drift your weight back onto your left leg (knee bent). Turn your right foot ninety degrees to the right (pivoting on your right heel) you are now facing the front again. Lift the heel of your left foot, you are now in Left Scissors stance.

At the same time cross your left arm over your right (see photograph). It is important that you do not lean forwards and strain your back. With your eyes you look at the end of the stick at the right hand side of your body.

Number 10

From Left Scissors stance, step with your left foot into Left Dragon stance, drifting your weight to the left side of your body. You are turning your body ninety degrees to the left, adjust your right foot (heel and toe).

At the same time as you move your feet, circle your left hand over until your right hand finishes by your right hip. The stick is angled upwards from your right hip (see photograph).

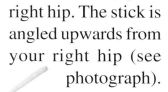

Number 11

From Left Dragon stance, drift your weight back onto your right side of your body bending your right knee. Turn your left foot ninety degrees to the right, next cross your right leg behind your left and raise the heel of your right foot, you are now in Right Scissors stance. You should once more be facing the front.

At the same time still holding your stick, cross your right arm over your left, remember not to strain your back by leaning forwards (see photograph). The stick should be angled just below the horizontal.

Number 12

From Right Scissors stance turn one hundred and eighty degrees to your right (facing the rear). To achieve this you pivot on the heel of your left foot and the ball of your right foot, then step sideways with your right foot

(placing your heel down first) you are now in Bear stance (feet shoulder width apart).

At the same time circle your right hand until it finishes in front of your right shoulder (palm facing away from you) and your left hand finishes in front of your left hip (the stick is diagonal across your body). See photograph.

Number 13

From Bear Stance turn one hundred and eighty degrees to your right into Riding Horse Stance (feet slightly wider than shoulder width apart, both knees bent).

At the same time, lift your left hand up as you turn, then lower it down. Your stick finishes horizontal (waist height) check your hand positions (left hand palm facing up, right hand palm facing down).

Number 14

From Riding Horse stance, drift your weight onto your right side, turn your left foot ninety degrees to the right (pivoting on the heel). Drift your weight onto your left leg, now raise your right leg into the air (bending your right knee, thigh parallel to the floor). You are now in Right Crane stance.

At the same time raise your right arm, your stick finishes inside your right thigh (see photograph). Left hand low -right hand high.

Number 15

From Right Crane stance turn one hundred and eighty degrees to your right (little jump) place your right foot down first, then step through with your left foot into Left Dragon stance, weight drifted across to the left hand side of your body (this is a two step movement).

At the same time circle your right hand down to your right hip (the stick is angled upwards from your right hip). Left hand high - right hand low.

Number 16

From Left Dragon stance drift your weight back onto your right leg, bending you right knee. At the same time straighten your left leg, you are now in Left Duck stance.

Your stick moves back with the movement of your body (see photograph).

Number 17

From Left Duck Stance, turn the heel of the left foot as far round to the right as it will go without strain. Drift your weight onto your left leg before turning 180 degrees to your right, this is achieved by picking up your right foot and placing it into position. Now drift your weight forward to your right leg, you are now in

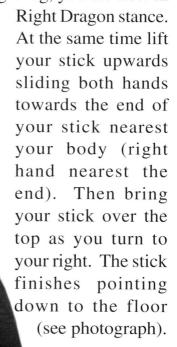

Right Dragon stance. At the same time lift your stick upwards sliding both hands towards the end of your stick nearest your body (right hand nearest the end). Then bring your stick over the top as you turn to your right. The stick finishes pointing down to the floor (see photograph).

Number 18

From Right Dragon Stance draw your left foot in half a pace, your right foot should be slightly in front of your left (both knees bent, weight evenly distributed between both legs) you are now in Right Snake stance.

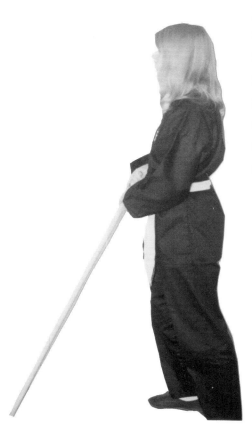

At the same time keeping your hands in the same position as they were in for number seventeen, draw a small clockwise circle with the free end of your stick.

Number 19

From Right Snake stance, bend your right knee slightly, then raise your left leg in the air (bending your left knee with the thigh parallel to the floor). You are now in Left Crane stance.

At the same time raise your right elbow as you draw your stick up through your left hand, your stick rotates by turning your right wrist so that your right palm faces to the right, then away from you as you complete the movement. Your stick finishes inside your left thigh (right hand high, palm facing away from you, left hand low, palm facing away from you).

Number 20

From Left Crane stance step forwards into Left Dragon stance, drifting the weight across to the left side of your body.

At the same time push your stick forwards through your left hand, allowing the stick to rotate by turning your right wrist so that your right palm faces left then upwards as you complete the movement. Simultaneously raising the left hand so that the stick finishes straight out in front of you at solar plexus level (see photograph).

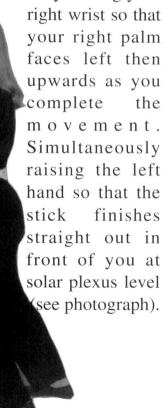

Number 21

From Left Dragon stance turn one hundred and eighty degrees to the right into Right Dragon stance. This is achieved by drifting your weight back on to your right leg, you will now be able to pivot on the heel of your left foot (turning right), next bend your left knee drifting your weight back on to it. Now pick up your right foot placing it in a Right Dragon stance and allow your weight to drift across to the right.

At the same time allow your left hand to slide along the stick away from the body. Lift the stick over as you turn into Right Dragon stance. Your right hand finishes underneath your left armpit (see photograph).

Number 22

From Right Dragon stance allow your weight to drift back onto your left leg, bend your left knee. Turn your right foot ninety degrees to the right (pivoting on your heel) place your weight onto it (bend your right knee)

now raise the heel on your left foot, you are now in Left Scissors stance.

At the same time cross your left arm over in front of your right arm, so that the stick is angle downwards, left hand low - right hand high and near to the body (see photograph).

Number 23

From Left Scissors stance take a little jump sideways
into Right Scissors stance. Remember to place your
left heel down first, your right leg is crossed behind
your left leg with your right heel lifted off the floor,
this is Right Scissors stance.

At the same time uncross your arms so that your left hand is palm facing up and your right hand is palm facing down (the stick is horizontal).

Number 24

From Right Scissors stance turn two hundred and seventy degrees clockwise to the right into Right Crane stance (turning on the heel of your left foot and the ball of your right foot). At the same time slide your right hand to the end of

your stick and the left one next to it, keep the stick close into the body as you make your turn (stick pointing down to the floor). When you have completed your 270 degrees turn, both hands should be palms facing up underneath the stick. Now raise your left elbow, moving your right hand underneath your left forearm (your left arm is wrapped around the front of your neck) your stick hangs behind your right shoulder, pointing downwards.

Number 25

From Right Crane stance, step behind into Left Monkey stance. Place your right heel down first allow your weight to drift across to the right, your left leg is straight, although not locked (raise the toes on your left foot).

At the same time pull the end of your stick downwards with your right hand, then allow it to slide down between your left hand to finish with the stick angled upwards from your right hip.

Number 26

From Left Monkey stance, turn one hundred and eighty degrees to your right into Right Dragon stance. This is achieved by pivoting on the heel of your left foot (turning 180 degrees to the right) and placing the toes flat on the floor. Now pick up your right foot and place it into Right Dragon stance.

At the same time change your hand position on your left hand (palm facing down) and circle your stick round to finish angled upwards from your right hip (see photograph).

Number 27

For movement number twenty seven stay in Right Dragon stance.

Circle the stick over to the left hand side of your body, so that it finishes angled upwards from your left hip.

Number 28

From Right Dragon stance step forwards with your left leg into Left Dragon stance, using the Taoist Walk.
At the same time change the hand position on your left hand so that it is underneath the stick (palm facing up).

Now circle your stick over and forwards until your right hand finishes underneath your left armpit.

Number 29

From Left Dragon Stance move your weight back onto the right leg, pivot on your left heel and turn one hundred and eighty degrees to your right into Right Duck stance (transfer your weight back onto your left

leg). Remember to use the Taoist walk, your right leg is straight and your left leg is bent.

Your stick remains in the same position as in number twenty eight .

Number 30

You remain in Right Duck stance for number thirty. Still holding your stick, move your right hand forwards and upwards, then bring your right hand back to your right shoulder (both palms are facing upwards).

Number 31

From Right Duck stance step forwards with your left foot into Left Cat stance (the ball of your left foot is resting lightly on the floor, your right knee is slightly bent).

At the same time circle your stick over to finish underneath your right armpit, your right arm is extended along the top of the stick. Left hand palm up, right hand palm down.

Number 32

From Left Cat stance raise your left leg into Left Crane stance (your right leg should be slightly bent to help your balance).

At the same time let go of your stick with your left hand and extend your left arm forward in front of your left shoulder (fingertips pointing to the ceiling). Still holding your stick with your right hand lower your right arm down by your right side (the stick is behind your right shoulder, see photograph).

Number 33

From Left Crane stance step forwards into Left Dragon stance, using the Taoist Walk.

At the same time extend your right arm forwards at shoulder height and return your left arm to the stick (underneath your right armpit,), palm facing up.

Number 34

From Left Dragon stance, step forwards and turn ninety degrees to your left into Riding Horse stance, moving your right foot first then correcting your left. Your feet should be slightly wider than shoulder width apart, both knees bent.

At the same time change your hand position on your right hand (palm faces to the left), stick finishes horizontal (left hand palm down, right hand palm up).

Number 35

From Riding Horse stance drift your weight across to the left now turn the heel of your right foot ninety degrees to the left (pivoting on your heel). Transfer your weight back on to your right leg and raise your left leg into Left Crane stance.

At the same time move your stick to finish inside your left thigh with your left hand high – right hand low, (see photograph).

Number 36

From Left Crane stance turn one hundred and eighty degrees to your left into Left Dragon stance.

At the same time bring your left hand down to your left hip, stick finishes a n g l e d upwards from left hip (see photograph).

Number 37

From Left Dragon stance raise your right leg into Right Crane stance (bending your left leg to aid your balance). At the same time allow your stick to angle downwards from your left hip (see photograph).

Number 38

From Right Crane stance turn ninety degrees to the right into Riding Horse stance (feet slightly wider than shoulder width apart, both knees bent).

At the same time change your hand position on your right hand (palm faces down) both hands finish palms facing down, your stick is horizontal.

Number 39

From Riding Horse stance turn one hundred and eighty degrees to the right into Left Scissors stance (turning on the heel of the right foot and the ball of the left).

Your stick remains in the same position.

Number 40

From Left Scissors stance turn ninety degrees to your left into Left Dragon stance, using your Taoist Walk.

At the same time circle your right arm upwards as you place your left hand on your left shoulder, (see photograph).

Number 41

From Left Dragon Stance step forwards with your right foot into Right Cat stance (the ball of your right foot should be lightly resting on the floor, your left knee should be slightly bent).

At the same time circle your right arm downwards until your right hand is underneath your left armpit (see photograph).

Number 42

From Right Cat stance place your right heel on the floor, bend your right knee and raise your left leg into Left Crane stance.

Your stick remains in the same position.

Number 43

Still in Left Crane stance turn one hundred and eighty degrees to your left.
The stick remains in the same position.

Number 44

From Left Crane stance, turn ninety degrees to your left crossing your left leg behind your right leg into Left Scissors stance (the ball of the left foot is resting lightly on the floor, the right knee is bent slightly).

At the same time let go of the stick with your right hand, extend it out sideways (shoulder height, fingertips pointing to the ceiling). Fold your left arm behind your back so the stick is angled from your left shoulder to your right hip.

Number 45

From Left Scissors stance turn ninety degrees to the left into Left Dragon stance (correct your right foot heel and toe).

At the same time take hold of the end of your stick near your left shoulder with your right hand (let go

with your left hand). Take your right hand to your right hip and replace your left hand onto the stick (stick angled upwards from the right hip), left hand palm up, right hand palm down.

Number 46

From Left Dragon stance turn ninety degrees to the left, this is achieved by picking up your right foot, taking it slightly behind as you turn your foot to the left. Your left foot slides round into Left Cat stance (the ball of your left foot is resting lightly on the floor).

At the same time circle your stick to the left hand side of your body (the stick is angled upwards from the left hip). Your left palm is facing up and your right palm is facing away from you.

Number 47

From Left Cat stance raise your left leg into Left Crane stance.

At the same time circle your left hand up and your right hand down. Your stick should finish inside your left thigh.

Number 48

From Left Crane stance step forward with your left leg into Left Dragon stance, using the Taoist Walk.

At the same time extend your right arm forwards allowing your left hand to move towards your left shoulder. Continue moving your right arm up and over until it finishes by your right hip, your left arm follows the movement (the stick finishes angled upwards from your right hip). This is the same stick movement as number six.

Number 49

From Left Dragon stance drift your weight across to your right side, bending your right knee and straightening your left leg. You are now in Left Duck stance.

Your stick moves back with the natural movement of your body.

Number 50

From Left Duck stance draw your left foot back to your right into Eagle stance (both heels together, toes pointing slightly outwards).

At the same time take your left arm underneath your right arm until your stick is behind your right shoulder. Now let go with your left hand and place it palm facing down near your right elbow (see photograph).

Number 51

From Eagle Stance step forwards with your left leg into Left Dragon stance, using the Taoist Walk.

At the same time move the end of your stick nearest to your right shoulder (downwards then underneath, over the top of your left hand) keeping your right hand turning until it comes to rest by your right hip. (Right hand palm facing down, your left hand turns palm facing up) the stick is angle upwards from your right hip.

Number 52

From Left Dragon stance cross your right leg behind your left, bend both knees and raise the heel on your right foot you are now in Right Scissors stance.

At the same time allow your stick to slide through your hands until it bangs on the floor at the right hand side of your body (both palms facing down). You are looking at the end of your stick.

Number 53

From Right Scissors stance place your right heel flat on the floor and step sideways with your left foot (placing your heel down first) into Left Leopard stance, using the Taoist Walk (your left leg is bent, your right leg is straight).

At the same time raise and pull the stick across to the left (eye level, looking along the stick) both hands palms down (see photograph).

Number 54

From Left Leopard stance turn ninety degrees to the right into Left Cat stance (the ball of your left foot should be resting lightly on the floor, your right knee is slightly bent).

At the same time the stick circles over until your right hand is underneath your left armpit.

Number 55

From Left Cat stance step behind with your left foot (placing your heel down first) allow your weight to drift back and straighten your right leg into Right Duck stance.

At the same time circle your stick until your left hand is on your left shoulder (see photograph).

Number 56

From Right Duck stance step behind with your right foot (placing your heel down first) drift the weight back onto your right side (straighten your left leg) you are now in Left Duck stance.

At the same time circle your stick so that your right hand is now on your right shoulder (see photograph).

Number 57

From Left Duck stance cross your right leg behind your left leg (bend both knees and raise the heel on your right foot) you are now in Right Scissors stance.

At the same time pull your stick across to the left hand side of your body, you are looking along your stick (see photograph).

Number 58

From Right Scissors stance place your right heel down and step sideways with your left foot into Left Leopard stance (placing your heel down first).

At the same time allow your stick to slide through your hands until it bangs on the floor at the right hand side of your body (see photograph).

Number 59

From Left Leopard stance cross your right leg in front of your left leg (bend both knees and raise the heel on your right foot) you are now in Right Cross Legs stance.

At the same time raise and push your stick out sideways to the left (see photograph).

Number 60

From Right Crossed Legs stance step off to your right into Right Leopard stance (placing your heel down first).

At the same time allow your stick to slide down between your hands until it bangs on the floor at the left hand side of your body (see photograph).

Number 61

From Right Leopard stance raise your right leg into Right Crane stance (bend your left knee slightly to help your balance).

At the same time draw your stick up until it finishes inside your right thigh (your right hand should be nearest the top of the stick).

Number 62

For number sixty two you remain in Right Crane stance.

At the same time circle the stick until your left hand is now nearest the top of the stick. Your stick finishes vertical inside your right thigh.

Number 63

From Right Crane stance turn one hundred and eighty degrees to your right into Right Dragon stance.

At the same time circle your stick over the top as you turn your body, the stick bangs on the floor in front of you (both hands are at the end of the stick, palms facing up, right hand nearest to your body).

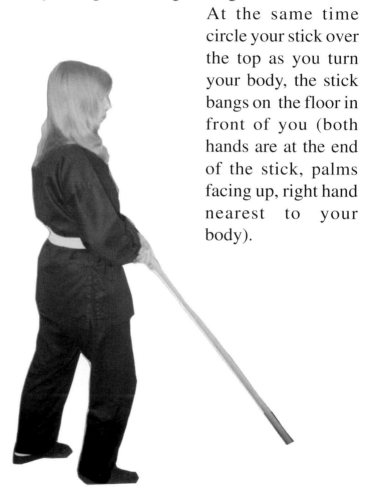

Number 64

From Right Dragon stance step behind with your right foot (placing your heel down first) drift your weight back, while at the same time straightening your left leg, you are now in Left Duck Stance.

At the same time draw your right arm back to your right hip and allow your stick to slide backwards and bang the floor. (See photograph).

Number 65

From Left Duck Stance raise your left leg into Left Crane stance (bending your right knee slightly to help your balance).

At the same time draw your stick up to finish inside your left thigh with your left hand nearest the top of your stick.

Number 66

From Left Crane stance step sideways (placing your left heel down first) into Left Leopard stance.

At the same time allow your stick to slide through your hands until it bangs on the floor at the right hand side of your body (see photograph).

Number 67

From Left Leopard stance turn ninety degrees to your right into Right Dragon stance (using the Taoist Walk and placing your heels down first).

At the same time place your left hand flat on the top of your stick, your right hand grips the stick (see photograph).

Number 68

For number sixty eight remain in Right Dragon stance.

At the same time change your hand position on your right hand so that your fingertips point to the left and your palm faces away from you (near the end of your stick closest to your body) place your left hand just below it (palm facing up). Now lift your stick so that it extends straight forward (solar plexus height).

Number 69

From Right Dragon stance step forwards with your left foot into Left Cat stance (the ball of your left foot is resting lightly on the floor, right knee bent).

At the same time lift and take your right elbow out sideways, pulling the stick through your left hand until 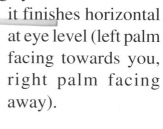 it finishes horizontal at eye level (left palm facing towards you, right palm facing away).

Number 70

From Left Cat stance place your left heel flat on the floor, pivot ninety degrees to your right and raise your right leg into Right Dog stance (left knee bent, right leg extended forwards).

At the same let go of your stick with your left hand and turn your stick as far round in an anti clockwise direction as your right wrist will allow. Place your left hand back on the stick (palm facing away from you) now remove and replace your right hand back onto the stick (palm facing towards you).

Number 71

From Right Dog stance place your right foot flat on the floor and raise the left leg behind (bent at the knee) into Left Stork stance.

At the same time let go of your stick with your left hand and allow the stick to slide through your right hand until it touches the floor. Your right hand grips your stick (palm facing to your left) your left hand rests on top of your stick (see photograph).

Number 72

From Left Stork stance turn one hundred and eighty degrees to your right into Right Stork stance. This is achieved with a little jump as you place your left foot down and raise your right leg (at the same time as you make your turn).

Your stick remains in the same position.

Number 73

From Right Stork stance turn forty five degrees to your left into Right Dragon stance you will need to adjust your left foot heel and toe.

At the same time change your hand position on your right hand (your fingertips point to your left, palm  facing away from you) now change your hand position on your left hand (both palms are now facing up) stick extended straight out in front of your body (see photograph).

Number 74

From Right Dragon stance step (backwards) into Right Leopard stance still on the diagonal.

At the same time pull your right elbow back (the stick rotates in your hands so that your (right hand is now palm facing down, left hand palm facing up). See photograph.

Number 75

From Right Leopard stance turn two hundred and twenty five degrees to your left into Right Crane stance (right leg raised with the knee bent) this achieved by pivoting on the heel of your left foot.

At the same time use your right arm (still holding the stick) to help you turn. Your stick finishes inside your right thigh (right hand nearest the top).

Number 76

From Right Crane stance, take your right leg directly behind you out into Right Hawk stance.

At the same time circle your right arm still holding the stick underneath your left arm pit.

Number 77

From Right Hawk stance, swing your right leg forwards turning ninety degrees to the left into Riding Horse stance (both knees bent, weight in the centre).

At the same time move your right hand from underneath your left arm (still holding the stick) to finish horizontal at waist height (right palm down, left palm up).

Number 78

From Riding Horse stance drift your weight across on to your left leg and come up into Right Crane stance. At the same time let go of the stick with your left hand, circling your stick with your right arm (palm facing up). Slide the stick underneath your right leg, now take hold of the stick with your left hand (palm facing down). Pull the stick through until the centre of the stick is underneath your right knee.

Number 79

From Right Crane stance, take your right foot behind your left leg raising your right heel into Right Scissors stance.

At the same time, let go of the stick with your right  hand. Pull the stick from underneath your right leg with your left hand. Now exchange your left hand for your right hand (near your right shoulder). Replace your left hand lower down the stick (palm facing down) your stick is angled downwards from your right shoulder to your left hip (see photograph).

Number 80

From Right Scissors stance place your right heel down and step sideways with your left foot (placing your heel down first) into Left Leopard stance (left knee bent right leg straight).

At the same time place your right hand at the right hand end of your stick, turn your left hand palm facing up. Now push your stick through your left hand, so that it is extended out sideways.

Number 81

From Left Leopard stance turn ninety degrees to the left into Right Crane stance, this is achieved by placing your weight onto your right side. (Pivot on the heel of your left foot, drift your weight back on to your left leg) now raise your right leg with your knee bent.

At the same time move your stick inside your right thigh (your right hand is nearest the top of your stick).

Number 82

From Right Crane stance, take your right leg out directly behind you into Right Hawk stance.

At the same time circle your right hand underneath your left arm pit (still holding your stick).

Number 83

From Right Hawk stance swing your right leg through into Right Dog stance. At the same time take your right hand forwards then back to your right shoulder (still holding your stick) both palms facing up.

Number 84

From Right Dog stance step behind into Left Chicken stance.

At the same time move your stick directly out in front of your body (stick rotates in your hands).

Number 85

From Left Chicken stance step behind with your left foot, drift your weight back and straighten your right leg, you are now in Right Duck stance.

At the same time allow your stick to slide between your hands, so that it hits the floor to the rear (right hand side) see photograph.

Number 86

From Right Duck stance turn your right foot ninety degrees to the right (pivoting on your right heel) place your weight onto your right leg and raise your left leg out sideways into Left Horse stance.

At the same time draw your stick up so that it extends sideways to the left across the front of the body (shoulder height).

Number 87

From Left Horse stance put your left foot down and turn ninety degrees to the right into Right Dragon stance.

At the same time circle your stick over the top until your stick touches the floor in front of you (your right hand is at the end of the stick and your left hand next to it).

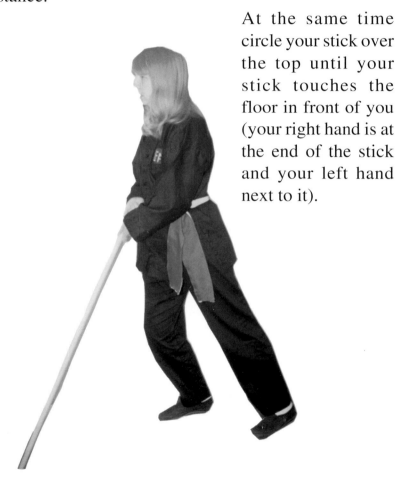

Number 88

From Right Dragon stance raise and take your left leg behind (bending your left knee) you are now in Left Stork stance.

At the same time move your hands so that they are in the same position they were in at number fifty.

Number 89

For movement eighty nine you remain in Left Stork stance.

Your hand movements with your stick are the same as number fifty one.

Number 90
From Left Stork stance step forwards into Left Dragon stance.

Your stick remains in
the same position.

Number 91

From Left Dragon stance step behind with your left foot into Right Duck stance drifting the weight back on to your left leg. At the same time still holding your stick, place your left hand on your right shoulder palm facing down. Your right arm is extended forwards from your right shoulder.

Number 92

Stay in Right Duck stance for movement number ninety two.

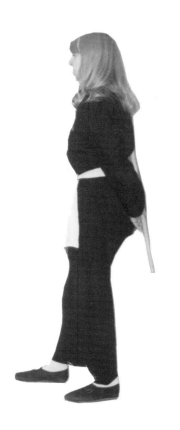

At the same time let go of your stick with your left hand, now slide your stick over your right shoulder so that it finishes angled from your right shoulder across your back to your left hip (take hold of your stick behind your back with your left hand). Left palm facing away from your body, right hand facing towards your body.

Number 93

From Right Duck stance come up into Left Crane stance (left leg raised with the knee bent)

At the same time let go of your stick with your right hand and pull your stick through in front of your body with your left hand. Your stick should finish inside your left thigh, your left hand is nearest the top of the stick (see photograph).

Number 94

From Left Crane stance step sideways with your left foot, drifting your weight across to the left (left knee bent, right leg straight) you are now in Left Leopard stance.

At the same time allow your stick to touch the floor at the right hand side of your body (see photograph).

Number 95

From Left Leopard stance turn ninety degrees to your right into Right Dragon stance, allowing your weight to drift across to your right leg.

At the same time allow your stick to move to the vertical position, placing your left hand on the top of it (like number sixty seven) grip the stick with your right hand (see photograph 67).

Number 96

Stay in Right Dragon stance for movement number ninety six.

At the same time change your hand positions so that both hands face palms up (right hand nearest the end of your stick). Your stick extends forward from your solar plexus (like number sixty eight).

Number 97

From Right Dragon stance step forward with your left foot into Left Cat stance (the ball of your left foot is resting lightly on the floor, your right knee is slightly bent).

At the same time pull your stick through your left hand until your stick is horizontal (eye level) left palm facing towards you, right palm facing away from you (like number sixty nine).

Number 98

From Left Cat Stance place your left heel flat on the floor then pivot ninety degrees to your right. Bend your left knee slightly and raise your right leg into Right Dog stance.

At the same time let go of your stick with your left hand and turn your stick as far round in an anti clockwise direction as your right wrist will allow. Place your left hand back on the stick palm facing away from you then replace your right hand on the stick so that your right palm faces towards you (like number seventy).

Number 99

From Right Dog stance move into Riding Horse stance (feet slightly wider than shoulder width apart, both knees bent).

At the same time lower your stick to waist height (right palm facing up, left palm facing down).

Number 100

For movement one hundred stay in Riding Horse stance.

At the same time with your left hand throw the end of your stick that is in your left hand towards your right hand, catching your stick so that your left palm is again facing down and your right palm up.

Number 101

From Riding Horse stance raise your right leg into Right Crane stance (right knee bent, thigh parallel to the floor).

At the same time let go of your stick with your right hand, exchanging your left hand for your right hand (right hand palm facing up). Now circle your stick underneath your right leg, replacing your left hand on the stick (palm facing down).

Number 102

From Right Crane stance extend your right leg forwards into Right Dog stance.

At the same time let go of your stick with your right hand, placing your left hand on your right shoulder (palm facing up). Replace your right hand back onto the stick (palm facing down) your stick is extended forwards.

Number 103

From Right Dog stance, take your right leg behind your left leg into Right Scissors stance.

At the same time pull your right arm back to extend sideways, your stick finishes horizontal at eye level (left palm facing up, right palm facing down).

Number 104

From Right Scissors stance turn ninety degrees to the right into Right Dragon stance.

At the same time let go of your stick with your left hand. With your right hand take the stick over the top (until the end hits the floor). Sliding your right hand nearer the end of your stick, replace your left hand back on to the stick (both hands palms facing up).

Number 105

From Right Dragon stance, raise your left leg into Left Stork stance (left knee bent, foot pointing behind you).

At the same time raise and rotate your stick to the left until your right hand finishes above your head (palm facing away from you). Your stick finishes at the outside edge of the left side of your body.

Number 106

From Left Stork stance, place your left foot flat on the floor and raise your right leg into Right Crane stance.

At the same time your right hand circles down and your left hand circles upwards until your stick finishes inside your right thigh.

Number 107

From Right Crane stance turn ninety degrees to the right into Right Dragon stance.

At the same time your right hand moves forwards and your left hand moves to your left shoulder (right hand palm facing down, left hand palm facing up).

Number 108

From Right Dragon stance, raise and extend your left leg out behind in Left Hawk stance.

At the same time your right arm circles underneath your left armpit. Your left arm is extended along the top of your stick.

Number 109

From Left Hawk stance swing your left leg forward into Left Dog stance.

Your stick remains in the same position for number one hundred and nine.

Number 110

From Left Dog stance, step through into Left Dragon stance.

Your stick remains in the same position for number one hundred and ten.

Number 111

From Left Dragon stance, step sideways with your right foot into Riding Horse stance (both knees bent).

At the same time circle your right hand slightly forwards then to the right to finish with your stick horizontal at shoulder height (left hand palm up, right hand palm down).

Number 112

From Riding Horse stance, raise your right leg out sideways into Right Horse stance.

At the same time place your left hand at the end of your stick and push your stick out sideways through your right hand, at shoulder height.

Number 113

From Right Horse stance place your right foot flat on the floor and come up into Left Stork stance (this time the left leg is wrapped around your right leg).

At the same time let go of your stick with your left hand, allow your stick to circle downwards to the floor at the right hand side of your body. Your left hand rests on top of the stick.

Number 114

From Left Stork stance, place your left foot on the floor and step sideways with your right foot into Riding Horse.

At the same time your right hand raises the stick to finish horizontal at shoulder height (palm facing down). Your left hand slides down underneath the stick, (palm facing up), pulling the stick across.

Number 115

From Riding Horse stance, cross your left leg behind your right leg into Left Scissors stance.

At the same time your right hand circles down and your left hand slides to the top of the stick. Your stick finishes touching the floor at the right hand side of your body.

Number 116

From Left Scissors stance place your left heel flat on the floor and step sideways into Riding Horse stance.

At the same time raise your right arm up to shoulder height so that your stick finishes horizontal (right palm facing down). Your left hand slides down underneath your stick (palm facing up), pulling the stick across.

Number 117

From Riding Horse stance raise your left leg into Left Stork stance.

At the same time circle your right hand down so that your stick finishes at the right hand side of your body. Your left hand slides to the end of your stick.

Number 118

From Left Stork stance, place your left heel flat on the floor and step sideways with your right foot into Riding Horse stance.

At the same time raise your right arm to shoulder height (palm facing down). Your left hand slides underneath the stick (palm facing up). The stick finishes on the diagonal from your right shoulder to your left hip.

Number 119

From Riding Horse stance, cross your left leg behind your right leg into Left Scissors stance.

At the same time raise your left arm to shoulder height so that your stick finishes horizontal (see photograph).

Number 120

From Left Scissors stance put your left heel flat on the floor and raise your right leg out sideways into Right Horse stance.

At the same time slide your left hand to the end of your stick and push the stick out sideways through your right hand.

Number 121

From Right Horse stance turn ninety degrees to the right into Right Stork stance.

At the same time circle your stick downwards until it come to rest on the floor, your left hand should still be on the end of the stick. Your stick finishes in the same position as number seventy two (see photograph).

Number 122

From Right Stork stance, step behind with your right leg into Left Duck stance (right knee bent, left leg straight).

At the same time raise your stick up to extend forwards from your solar plexus (both palms facing up).

Number 123

From Left Duck stance step behind with your left foot into Right Duck stance (left knee bent, right leg straight).

At the same time allow your stick to slide through your hands until it hits the floor at the right hand side of your body and slightly to the rear (left hand palm up, right hand palm facing down).

Number 124

From Right Duck stance step behind with your right leg into Left Duck stance (right knee bent, left leg straight).

At the same time change the hand position on your left hand and circle your stick over to the left hand side of your body (stick finishes angled up from your left hip).

Number 125

From Left Duck stance step behind with your left leg into Right Duck stance (right leg straight, left knee bent).

At the same time circle your stick over to the right hand side of your body (your stick finishes angled upwards from your right hip).

Number126

From Right Duck stance turn ninety degrees to the right into Riding Horse stance (both knees bent).

At the same time your left hand lowers until your stick finishes horizontal at waist height. Your right hand turns palm facing up.

Number 127

From Riding Horse stance turn one hundred and eighty
degrees to your right staying in Riding Horse stance.

At the same time
your stick raises to
shoulder height.
Your left hand turns
palm facing up.

Number 128

From Riding Horse stance, turn ninety degrees to the right into Left Hawk stance (left leg raised and extended behind).

At the same time your right hand circles underneath your left armpit. Your left arm extends along the top of your stick.

Number 129

From Left Hawk stance turn one hundred and eighty degrees to your right still in Left Hawk stance.

Your stick remains in the same position for number one hundred and twenty nine.

Number 130

From Left Hawk stance, step through into Left Dragon Stance.

At the same time your right arm extends forwards and your left hand finishes on your left shoulder.

Number 131

From Left Dragon stance, step through into Right Dragon stance (using the Taoist walk).

At the same time your right hand circles down and in, to finish with your stick extended forwards from your solar plexus (right hand near the end of your stick, both palms facing up).

Number 132

From Right Dragon stance, step though with your left leg into Left Dragon stance.

At the same time pull your right hand back to your right hip, your stick finishes angled upwards from your right hip.

Number 133

From Left Dragon stance stance, swing your right leg through into Right Dog stance.

At the same time both hands move to the end of your stick. Your stick finishes extended forwards from your solar plexus.

Number 134

From Right Dog stance, turn one hundred & eighty degrees to the right into Right Dragon stance.

At the same time your stick circles over the top and hits the floor in front of your body (both hands remain in the same position).

Number 135

From Right Dragon stance lower your weight into Right Chicken stance.

At the same time your stick raises to extend forwards from your solar plexus (both palms facing up).

Number 136

From Right Chicken stance, turn ninety degrees to the right into Left Scissors stance.

At the same time draw the stick up through your left hand to finish at the left hand side of your body (your right forearm is above your head).

Number 137

From Left Scissors stance, place your left heel flat on the floor. Step to the side with your right foot into Riding Horse stance.

At the same time lower your right arm down until your stick finishes horizontal at waist height (right palm down, left palm up).

Number 138

From Riding Horse stance, move into Bear stance.

At the same time your right hand moves up to shoulder height, your left hand moves down to your left hip so that your stick finishes angled downwards from right to left.

Number 139

From Bear stance turn ninety degrees to your right, raise your left leg into Left Crane stance (left knee bent, thigh parallel to the floor).

At the same time your stick moves inside your left thigh (right hand high, left hand low).

Number 140

From Left Crane stance, turn ninety degrees to your right into Left Scissors stance.

At the same time your right hand moves slightly across to your right so that your stick finishes angled downwards from above the right hand side of your head to your left shoulder.

Number 141

From Left Scissors stance step sideways into Right Leopard stance (right knee bent, left leg straight).

At the same time allow your stick to slide through your hands until it hits the floor at the left hand side of your body.

Number 142

From Right Leopard stance, cross your left leg in front of your right into Left Crossed Legs stance.

At the same time raise and slide your stick through your hands to finish at shoulder height extended to the right (see photograph).

Number143

From Left Crossed Legs stance step sideways (left) into Left Leopard stance.

At the same time allow the stick to slide through your hands and hit the floor at the right hand side of your body.

Number 144

From Left Leopard stance, turn two hundred and seventy degrees to the right into Right Stork stance (stepping over your stick).

At the same time your left hand moves to the end of your stick (palm down). Your right hand grips hold of the stick (see photograph).

Number 145

From Right Stork stance, swing your right leg forwards into Right Dog stance.

At the same time swing your stick upwards to extend forwards from your solar plexus (both hands palms up).

Number 146

From Right Dog stance turn one hundred and eighty degrees to the right into Left Hawk stance.

At the same time your left hand slides along the stick, as you bring your stick over the top. Your right hand finishes underneath your left arm pit.

Number 147

From Left Hawk stance swing your left leg down into Eagle stance (heels together, toes pointing slightly outwards).

At the same time circle your right hand down, then up to finish in front of your right shoulder. Your left hand finishes near your left hip.

Number 148

Stay in Eagle stance for number one hundred and forty eight.

At the same time allow your right hand to circle down to your right side. Your left hand slides to the end of the stick, pushing it through your right hand until it hits the floor.

Number 149

Stay in Eagle stance for number one hundred and forty nine.

At the same time raise your stick until the left hand is near the left shoulder and your right hand is near your right hip.

Number 150

Stay in Eagle stance for number one hundred and fifty.

At the same time circle your left hand down to your left side. Allow your right hand to slide to the end of your stick, pushing the stick through your left hand until it hits the floor at your left side.

The LFA T'ai Chi Stick Set is for everyone, this book acts as a beginners guide. To find the inner depth taught within the movements, you may wish to train with us at one of the ever growing number of LFA classes and day courses.

A list of which is available on our Website
www.leefamilyarts. com

I hope you have enjoyed learning the first one hundred and fifty movements of our Stick Set, we intend to publish the remainder of the movements in a future book. May you continue to enjoy the journey of the Lee Family Arts.

Best Regards
Sheila Dickinson
LFA President

LFA T'AI CHI STICK

Notes

LFA T'AI CHI STICK

Notes